The Gingerbread Boy

WRITTEN BY
VIVIAN FRENCH

ILLUSTRATED BY
JOHN PRATER

WALKER BOOKS
AND SUBSIDIARIES
LONDON • BOSTON • SYDNEY • AUCKLAND

First published 2000 by Walker Books Ltd, 87 Vauxhall Walk, London SE11 5HJ

This edition published 2012

2 4 6 8 10 9 7 5 3 1

This book has been typeset in Century Old Style

Printed in China

British Library Cataloguing in Publication Data:
a catalogue record for this book is available from the British Library

ISBN 978-1-4063-4334-2

www.walker.co.uk

Notes for Children

The Gingerbread Boy is the story of a naughty boy made of gingerbread who runs and runs until he meets a clever fox. You may know the story already, but it doesn't matter if you don't.

This book is a little different from other picture books. You will be sharing it with other people and telling the story together.

You can read

this line

this line

this line

or this line.

Even when someone else is reading, try to follow the words. It will help when it's your turn!

"I can skip, I can hop

I'm my mother's pride and joy

But you can't catch me

I'm the Gingerbread Boy!"

I know that story.

I know that story too!

Once upon a time

There was a little old woman –

No! It was a little old man.

No! It was a little old woman.

It was a little old woman

AND a little old man.

They lived in a house

A little old house

And they were lonely.

No little girls.

No little boys.

So the little old woman said,

“I will mix, I will bake

I will make a little cake.”

No! Not a cake.

That’s right. Not a cake.

Sorry!

She said,

“I will mix, I will bake

And guess what I will make!"

And the little old man said,

"A GINGERBREAD BOY!"

So the little old woman mixed

And she mixed and she mixed

And she made

A Gingerbread Boy!

He had currant eyes

And a currant nose

And she put him in the oven.

She put him in the oven to bake.

Was it hot?

Very hot.

And the little old woman said,

"Soon we will have our own little boy.

Our own little Gingerbread Boy."

And the little old man said, "Good."

When the Gingerbread Boy was cooked

The little old woman took him out.

Out of the oven.

Was he hot?

Very hot.

And the little old woman said,

"Hullo, Gingerbread Boy."

And the little old man said,

"Hullo, Gingerbread Boy."

And the Gingerbread Boy said,

"Hullo, Mother. Hullo, Father."

Then the Gingerbread Boy said,
"I can skip, I can hop
I'm my mother's pride and joy
But you can't catch me
I'm the Gingerbread Boy!"

And the Gingerbread Boy ran away

Away from the little old woman

Away from the little old man.

They both ran after him shouting, “STOP!”

But the Gingerbread Boy wouldn’t stop.

He ran and he ran.

He ran under the gate

And into a field

And there in the field

Was a black and white cow.

And the cow said,

"Oink! Oink! Oink!"

Ho ho. Very funny.

The cow said,

"Come here, little Gingerbread Boy

Because I want to eat you all up!"

But the Gingerbread Boy said,

"I can skip, I can hop

I'm my mother's pride and joy

But you can't catch me

I'm the Gingerbread Boy!"

And the Gingerbread Boy ran away

Away from the cow

Away from the little old woman

Away from the little old man

And they all ran after him shouting, "STOP!"

But the Gingerbread Boy wouldn't stop.

He ran and he ran.

He ran under the fence

And up the hill

And there on the hill

Was a sheep.

And the sheep said,

"Woof! Woof! Woof!"

You've done that joke before.

Sorry! The sheep said,

"Come here, little Gingerbread Boy

Because I want to eat you all up!"

But the Gingerbread Boy said,

"I can skip, I can hop

I'm my mother's pride and joy

But you can't catch me

I'm the Gingerbread Boy!"

And the Gingerbread Boy ran away

Away from the sheep

Away from the cow

Away from the little old woman

Away from the little old man.

They all ran after him shouting, “STOP!”

But the Gingerbread Boy wouldn’t stop.

He ran and he ran.

He ran down the hill

And down to the lane

And there in the lane

Was a chicken.

And the chicken said, “Cluck! Cluck! Cluck!”

That’s not fair!

What’s not fair?

I do the clucks.

Well, I wanted to. I like chickens.

Can we get on with the story?

The chicken said,

"Come here, little Gingerbread Boy

Because I want to eat you all up!"

But the Gingerbread Boy said,

"I can skip, I can hop

I'm my mother's pride and joy

But you can't catch me

I'm the Gingerbread Boy!"

And the Gingerbread Boy ran away

Away from the chicken –

Cluck! Cluck!

Away from the sheep –

Baa! Baa!

Away from the cow –

Moo! Moo!

Away from the little old woman

Away from the little old man

And they all ran after him shouting, “STOP!”

“STOP! STOP! STOP! STOP!”

But the Gingerbread Boy wouldn't stop,

He ran and he ran.

He ran under the bushes

And into the woods

And there in the woods

Was a fox!

And the fox said,

"Hullo, little Gingerbread Boy.

How fast you can run!"

And the Gingerbread Boy said,

"I can skip, I can hop —"

And the fox said,

"Yes, yes, yes – but can you swim?"

And the Gingerbread Boy said,

"Swim?"

"Yes," said the fox. "Swim over the river."

The Gingerbread Boy said,

"Why do I want to swim over the river?"

And the fox said,

"If you swim over the river, the chicken –

Cluck! Cluck!

And the sheep –

Baa! Baa!

And the cow –

Moo! Moo!

And the little old woman

And the little old man

Will never ever be able to catch you."

Then the Gingerbread Boy said,

“I want to go over the river

But I can’t swim.”

“Jump on my tail,” said the fox. “I’ll take you.”

So the Gingerbread Boy

Jumped on the fox's tail

And the fox jumped into the river.

The fox swam and swam. Splish! Splash!

The Gingerbread Boy said, "I'm getting wet!"

The fox said, "Jump on my back."

The fox swam and swam. Splish! Splash!

The Gingerbread Boy said,

"I'm still getting wet!"

The fox said, "Jump on my head."

And the fox swam up to the shore.

He jumped right out of the river

And he shook his head

And tossed the Gingerbread Boy up in the air

And ate him all up –

YUM! YUM! YUM!

Notes for Teachers

Story Plays are written and presented in a way that encourages children to read aloud together. They are dramatic versions of memorable and exciting stories, told in strongly patterned language which gives children the chance to practise at a vital stage of their reading development. Sharing stories in this way makes reading an active and enjoyable process, and one that draws in even the reticent reader.

The story is told by four different voices, divided into four colours so that each child can easily read his or her part. The blue line is for more experienced readers; the red line for less experienced readers. When there are more than four children in a group, there is an ideal opportunity for paired reading. Partnering a more experienced reader with a less experienced one can be very supportive and provides a learning experience for both children.

Story Plays encourage children to share in the reading of a whole text in a collaborative and interactive way. This makes them perfect for group and guided reading activities. Children will find they need to pay close attention to the print and punctuation, and to use the meaning of the whole story in order to read it with expression and a real sense of voice.